The Owl and the Pussycat

Edward Lear
Illustrated by Victoria Ball

Reading Consultant: Alison Kelly
Roehampton University

The Owl and the
Pussycat went to sea

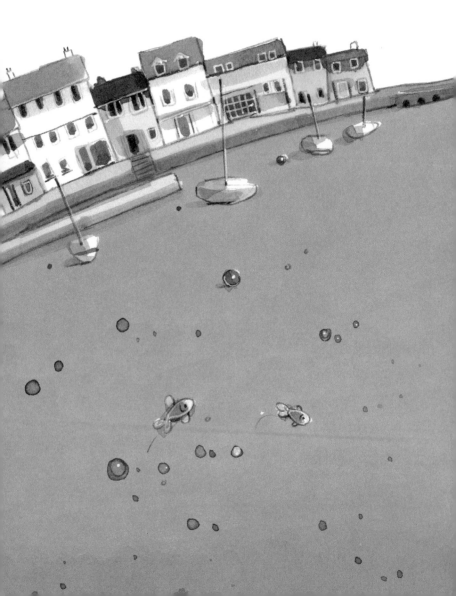

in a beautiful
pea-green boat.

They took some honey

and plenty
of money,

£5

wrapped up in a
five pound note.

The Owl looked up to
the stars above and sang
to a small guitar.

Oh lovely Pussy!
Oh Pussy my love...

What a beautiful
Pussy you are, you are,

what a beautiful
Pussy you are.

Pussy said to the Owl,

you elegant fowl,

how charmingly sweet
you sing.

Oh let us be married –
too long we have tarried.

But what shall we do
for a ring?

They sailed away...

...for a year and a day,

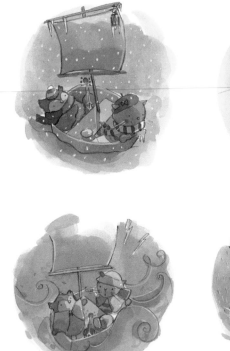

to the land where the
Bong-tree grows.

And there in the wood

a Piggy-wig stood,

with a ring at the end
of his nose,

his nose,

with a ring at the end
of his nose.

Dear Pig, are you willing,

to sell for one shilling,

your ring?

Said the Piggy,

I will!

So they took it away,

and were married
next day,

by the turkey who lives
on the hill.

They dined on mince, and
slices of quince,

which they ate with a
runcible spoon.

And hand in hand,

on the edge of the sand,

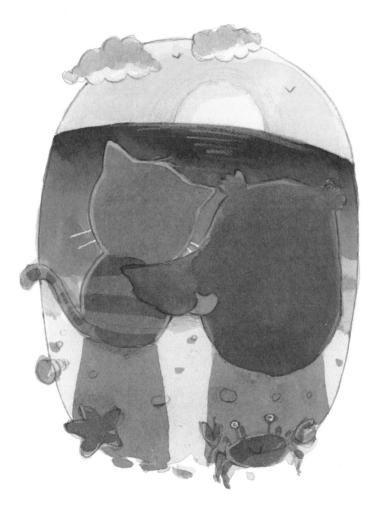

they danced by the
light of the moon,

the moon,

they danced by the light
of the moon.